Other titles in the series:
The World's Greatest Business Cartoons
The World's Greatest Cat Cartoons
The World's Greatest Computer Cartoons
The World's Greatest Dad Cartoons
The World's Greatest Do-It-Yourself Cartoons
The World's Greatest Golf Cartoons
The World's Greatest Keep-Fit Cartoons
The World's Greatest Marriage Cartoons
The World's Greatest Middle Age Cartoons

Published simultaneously in 1995 by Exley Publications
in Great Britain, and Exley Giftbooks in the USA.

12 11 10 9 8 7 6 5 4 3 2 1

ISBN 1-85015-624-7

Front cover illustration by Roland Fiddy.
Designed by Pinpoint Design.
Edited by Mark Bryant.
Printed and bound by Grafo, S.A., Bilbao, Spain.

Exley Publications Ltd, 16 Chalk Hill, Watford, Herts WD1 4BN, UK.
Exley Giftbooks, 232 Madison Avenue, Suite 1206, NY 10016, USA.

THANK YOU

We would like to thank all the cartoonists who submitted entries for *The World's Greatest SEX CARTOONS*. They came in from many parts of the world – including New Zealand, Romania, Israel and Russia.

Special thanks go to the cartoonists whose work appears in the final book. They include Ros Asquith pages 32, 53; Les Barton pages 61, 67; Clive Collins page 42; Orhan Doğu page 36; John Donegan page 26; Stan Eales pages 14, 30, 43, 69; Stidley Easel pages 6, 9, 18, 66, 75; Noel Ford pages 20, 41, 54; Martin Honeysett page 73; Tony Husband pages 4, 7, 11, 16, 22, 25, 28, 35, 38, 40, 44, 47, 51, 55, 58, 60, 71, 78; Mik Jago pages 17, 49; David Myers pages 10, 34; Constantin Pavel page 31; Ken Pyne page 46; Viv Quillin pages 5, 8, 12, 15, 19, 21, 24, 27, 29, 37, 39, 45, 48, 52, 56, 59, 62, 65, 70, 72, 74, 76, 79; Bryan Reading pages 23, 50, 63; Alex Talimonov page 57; Geoff Thompson pages 64, 77; Colin Whittock pages 13, 33, 68.

Every effort has been made to trace the copyright holders of cartoons in this book. However, any error will gladly be corrected by the publisher for future printings.

THE WORLD'S GREATEST

SEX

CARTOONS

EDITED BY
Mark Bryant

EXLEY
NEW YORK • WATFORD UK

So we kick off with 15 minutes' increasing-awareness-by-massage, then "Hello to our genitalia".. 5 minutes either way?

don't forget BONDING time afterwards

© Quillin.

5

"There must have been a hole in the condom."

"Oi, sod off!"

"OK, which of you guys knows how to make
a virtual–reality sex-machine?"

9

"Don't you think you could remove that now?"

"I can tell that you're mentally undressing me."

"We're doing biology at school and the teacher
wants us to find out what position you prefer."

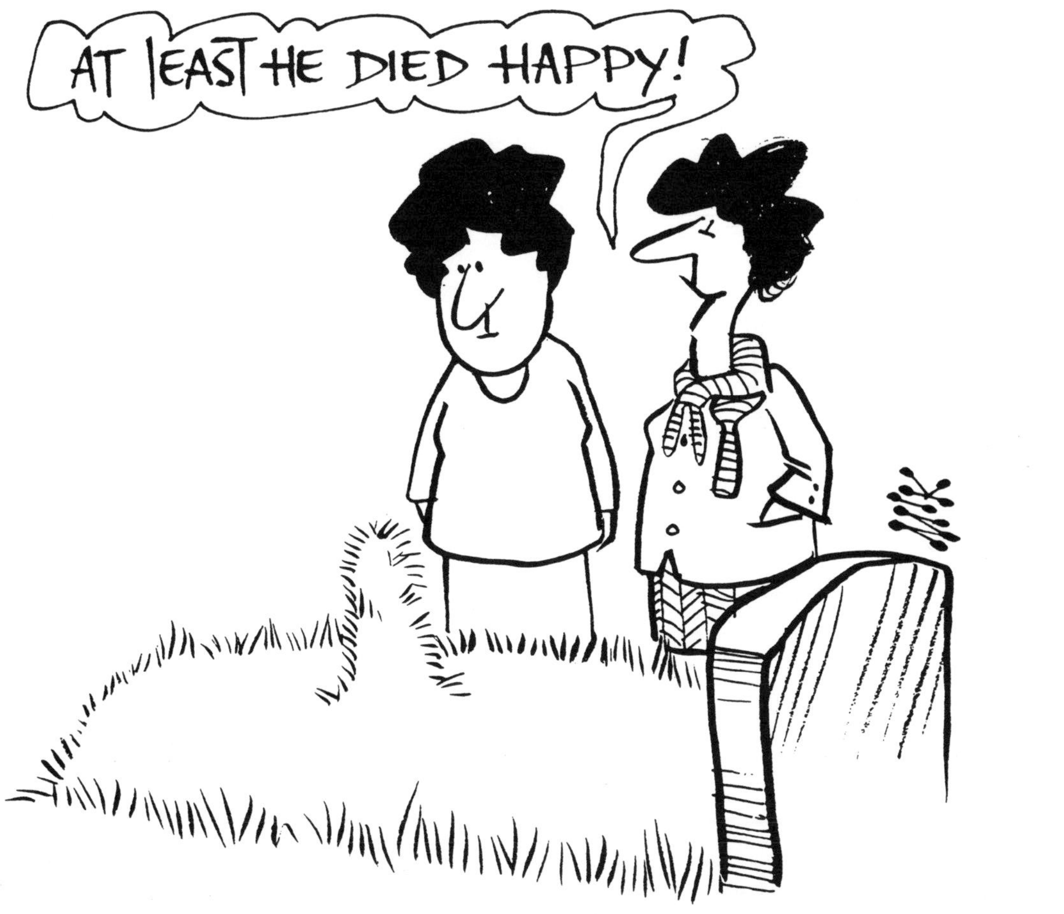
AT LEAST HE DIED HAPPY!

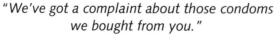

*"We've got a complaint about those condoms
we bought from you."*

"I didn't say we wanted to <u>go</u> anywhere, Dad –
I just asked if we could use the car."

"That reminds me, how's your husband?"

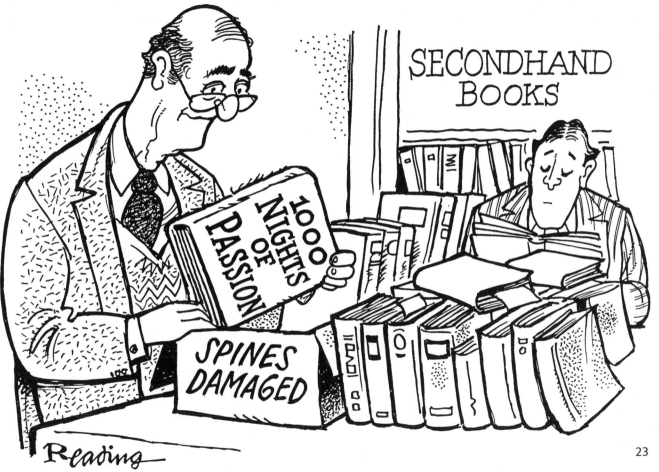

"Father, I have sinned, I can't stop teasing men."

"What would you recommend for a seduction scene?"

"For goodness sake woman,
what's wrong with the wallpaper?"

C. PAVEL

"You've been reading those manuals again . . . !"

"Skip the bees - just tell me about the birds."

"Er Helen, I was wondering if there's
a more subtle way of letting me know."

1.

2.

3.

"Sorry, I'm a little hard of hearing,
can you heavy-breathe louder?"

by now you are relaxed and eager for sex

© Quillin.

39

"'Scuse me, what would I get for my pet toad Eric,
a badge and two marbles?"

"Miss Framley and I have pleasure in announcing an office scandal . . ."

"Brian, lots of men have small privates,
take Nigel here!"

"This is my bed-sit."

"Before you go home, Ms Lomax, take a letter."

I'm leaving you Sandra - to go in search
of my dream girl - always ready for
sex ... but
only when I
want it

48

"I preferred the frog!"

"I'll tell him about sex if you like, Miss Pettifer,
but he might find your version a bit more convincing."

"I wanted to get away from the
traditional chairman's portrait."

53

"But surely it's not sex discrimination from me to insist on a *GIRL*?"

"George's idea of foreplay is to feed the budgie
before we go to bed."

56

A-94

"When we were your age sex wasn't such a big issue with us.
In fact it's not much of an issue now either."

The Tragedy of the Solar–powered Vibrator

"I forget, do we have sex on the first
or second Saturday of the month?"

"Reception? Could you send up another nine Gideon Bibles!"

"It's not my idea of a fertility rite."

"It works! . . . It works!"

"What do you mean, you were revising
'Practical Biology' ?"

Sex? Well I've got a window in my schedule late next week
© Quillin.

"Couldn't we have garden gnomes like everyone else?"

"*Actually they're no bigger at all,
but we sell an awful lot of them.*"

"Yes, this is me. Hello . . . Pastor Williams!
Well, how . . . er . . . surprising to hear from you."

"You only want me for my body."

"I think my wife suspects us."

it's page 93.. there's
nothing about how to undo
yourself. Ring the publisher
for God's sake!

Books in "The World's Greatest" series
($4.99 £2.99 paperback)

The World's Greatest Business Cartoons
The World's Greatest Cat Cartoons
The World's Greatest Computer Cartoons
The World's Greatest Dad Cartoons
The World's Greatest Do-It-Yourself Cartoons
The World's Greatest Golf Cartoons
The World's Greatest Keep Fit Cartoons
The World's Greatest Middle Age Cartoons
The World's Greatest Marriage Cartoons
The World's Greatest Sex Cartoons

Books in the "Victim's Guide" series
($4.99 £2.99 paperback)

Award-winning cartoonist Roland Fiddy sees the funny side of life's phobias, nightmares and catastrophes.

The Victim's Guide to Air Travel
The Victim's Guide to the Baby
The Victim's Guide to Christmas
The Victim's Guide to the Dentist
The Victim's Guide to the Doctor
The Victim's Guide to Middle Age

Books in the "Crazy World" series
($4.99 £2.99 paperback)

The Crazy World of Aerobics (Bill Stott)
The Crazy World of Cats (Bill Stott)
The Crazy World of Cricket (Bill Stott)
The Crazy World of Gardening (Bill Stott)
The Crazy World of Golf (Mike Scott)
The Crazy World of the Handyman (Bill Stott)
The Crazy World of Hospitals (Bill Stott)

The Crazy World of Housework (Bill Stott)
The Crazy World of Learning To Drive (Bill Stott)
The Crazy World of Love (Roland Fiddy)
The Crazy World of Marriage (Bill Stott)
The Crazy World of The Office (Bill Stott)
The Crazy World of Photography (Bill Stott)
The Crazy World of Rugby (Bill Stott)
The Crazy World of Sailing (Peter Rigby)
The Crazy World of Sex (David Pye)
The Crazy World of Soccer (Bill Stott)

The "Fanatic's" series
($4.99 £2.99 paperback)

The **Fanatic's Guides** are perfect presents for everyone with a hobby that has got out of hand. Eighty pages of hilarious black and white cartoons by Roland Fiddy.

The Fanatic's Guide to the Bed
The Fanatic's Guide to Cats
The Fanatic's Guide to Computers
The Fanatic's Guide to Dads
The Fanatic's Guide to Diets
The Fanatic's Guide to Dogs
The Fanatic's Guide to Golf
The Fanatic's Guide to Husbands
The Fanatic's Guide to Money
The Fanatic's Guide to Sex
The Fanatic's Guide to Skiing
The Fanatic's Guide to Sports

Great Britain: Order these super books from your local bookseller or From Exley Publications Ltd, 16 Chalk Hill, Watford, Herts WDI 4BN. (Please send £1.30 to cover post and packaging on 1 book, £2.60 on 2 or more books.)